by

J. Chatwin

BERNARD BABANI (publishing) LTD
THE GRAMPIANS
SHEPHERDS BUSH ROAD
LONDON W6 7NF
ENGLAND

Please Note

Although every care has been taken with the production of this book to ensure that any projects, designs, modifications and/or programs, etc., contained herewith, operate in a correct and safe manner and also that any components specified are normally available in Great Britain, the Publishers do not accept responsibility in any way for the failure, including fault in design, of any project, design, modification or program to work correctly, or to cause damage to any other equipment that it may be connected to or used in conjunction with, or in respect of any other damage or injury that may be so caused, nor do the Publishers accept responsibility in any way for the failure to obtain specified components.

Notice is also given that if equipment that is still under warranty is modified in any way or used or connected with home-built equipment then that warranty may be void.

© 1995 BERNARD BABANI (publishing) LTD

First Published — February 1995

British Library Cataloguing in Publication Data
    Chatwin, J.
    Projects for the Electric Guitar
    I. Title
    787.8719028

    ISBN 0 85934 358 8

Printed and Bound in Great Britain by Cox & Wyman Ltd, Reading

Contents

Preface

This book is intended for anyone interested in the electric guitar who would like to learn how to modify or customise the electronics side of the instrument.

The first part of the book covers the basic electronic functions of the instrument, such as pickups and tone controls, and has numerous examples of working circuits, including guitar wiring diagrams and specialised switching suggestions.

The second section contains a number of active circuit projects designed mainly for installation inside instruments. These range from simple tone modifiers to a notch filter and active equaliser for an acoustic guitar.

Please note that due to the printing process used in the production of this book, the absolute accuracy of the dimensions of the PCB patterns can not be guaranteed and should be regarded as a guide only.

John Chatwin, October 1994

Other Titles of Interest

Chapter 1

PICKUPS

Types of Pickups

Electric guitars are designed to be amplified, and while the quality of the materials that an instrument is made of, and how it is put together determine the way it plays, the pickup is the first component in the amplification chain, and so has a major effect on the way it actually sounds. No matter how beautifully made an instrument may be, if the pickup is no good it will sound awful.

The function of the pickup (sometimes called a transducer) is simply to convert the mechanical vibrations of the strings into electrical impulses which can then be amplified. There are scores of different types available, but they generally fall into one of two categories:

— *Electromagnetic*, which sense only string vibrations; and
— *Piezo-electric*, which will pick up any mechanical vibration.

Almost all electric guitars, apart from a few exotic variations, have the electromagnetic type (Fig.1.1). Acoustic guitars, if they are to be amplified directly, tend to be fitted with piezo-electric pickups, because the overall sound of the instrument, and not just the strings, needs to be reproduced. The ability of piezos to capture the whole sound also makes them good for violins and cellos, as well as other instruments that have non-metallic strings.

The Electromagnetic Pickup

Electromagnetic pickups are basically very simple, and consist of a coil of copper wire wound onto a thin former surrounding a central magnetic core. Often a former isn't used, and the coil is wound directly onto the core. This enables the windings to be as close as possible to the magnets, which produces a higher output from the pickup and better high frequency response.

The pickup assembly is mounted in a recess cut into the guitar body so that the strings pass through the magnetic

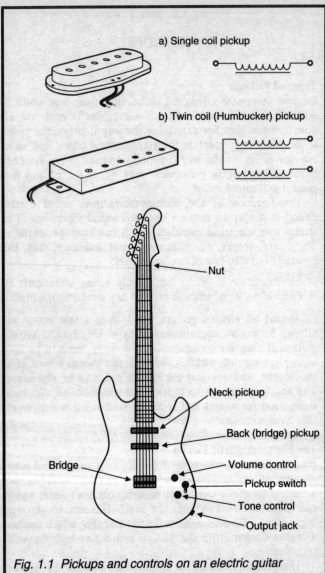

a) Single coil pickup

b) Twin coil (Humbucker) pickup

Nut

Neck pickup

Back (bridge) pickup

Bridge

Volume control

Pickup switch

Tone control

Output jack

Fig. 1.1 Pickups and controls on an electric guitar

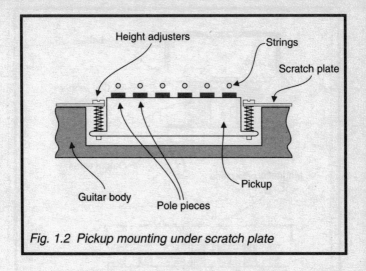

Fig. 1.2 Pickup mounting under scratch plate

field that extends above the core (Fig.1.2). When the strings are plucked, their vibrations inside the field induce currents in the coil. These currents, which are very small at this point, can be fed from the guitar to an external amplifier.

The coil and magnet arrangement sounds very simple, and if it were merely a case of getting sound from a guitar, it would be, but in practice pickups have to be carefully designed and made to a high degree of accuracy if they are to produce a consistently good sound. This becomes more important when mass production is involved.

Figure 1.3 is a diagram of a normal electromagnetic pickup. You'll notice that the coil is formed around six magnets. Each one has its north and south poles facing in the same direction. This is important because if some of the poles pointed the other way a distorted field would be created around the coil, and the pickup would sound uneven. You may find it useful to mark the poles if you take a pickup apart to modify or repair it, as this can make things a lot easier when you come to put it back together.

If a guitar has two or more pickups, they need to be arranged so that they have similar poles facing the strings to avoid problems with phase relationships between the coils

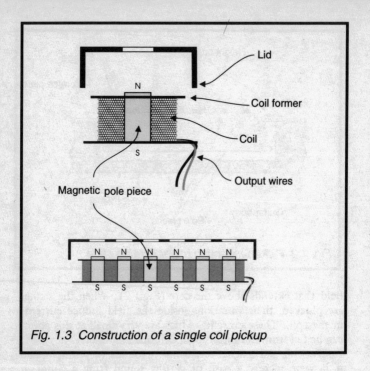

Fig. 1.3 Construction of a single coil pickup

when both pickups are on together.

Not all pickups have the six magnet arrangement. Many of the cheaper types make do with a single magnet positioned under the coil (Fig.1.4). This is formed around a steel bar which takes on the properties of the magnet and becomes, in effect, one of its poles. Adjustment screws are sometimes fitted so that a rough balance can be made between the relative volumes of the strings, though the effectiveness of these is limited.

If you need a higher output from a pickup, you should try raising it closer to the strings so that they can have more effect on the magnetic field. In designs that use some of the more powerful ceramic nagnets, however, adjusting them too far up can have a dampening effect, especially on light strings. Certain early types of pickup were prone to this type of problem, and later models had modified pole pieces to

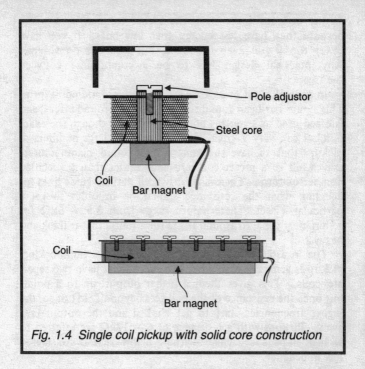

Fig. 1.4 Single coil pickup with solid core construction

compensate for the varying effects that different string gauges produced.

The main factors that determine how a pickup will sound are the number of turns in the coil, the resistance or impedance of the coil, and the thickness of the wire used to form it. How strong the magnets are is also important, as is the way the coil is wound.

An even coil will have more turns close to the core than one that is bunched up or wound randomly, and will therefore have a greater output. Pickup coils are usually wound from fine resin or enamel coated copper wire of 38 – 42 SWG, which is thin enough to enable several thousand turns to be crammed inside the case. The actual number of turns is important because it determines the resistance of the unit and affects its tonal range and output. The more turns, the higher the output, but the lower the frequency response –

as the coil resistance rises, the higher frequencies are lost because they have less energy than low ones. If you have fewer turns, you keep the treble but lose out on volume. Any practical design has to be a compromise between the two.

In general, a lot of pickups end up with around 6500 turns. This figure has been found to give a good all-round effect, and is often used as a starting point by designers, though the exact number can vary a great deal. To produce large numbers of pickups that all have the same sort of sound, manufacturers may wind to a preset coil resistance rather than a specified number of turns. There are fairly well defined guide lines for deciding what the resistance should be in order to get a particular effect. These values range from $3.5 - 6k\Omega$ for a thin clear tone, to around $14k\Omega$ for a sound that is thick and heavy.

The resistance of a noise cancelling, or 'humbucking' pickup is generally higher because these units have two separate coils. This gives them a higher output, up to a point, but once the resistance of the coil gets beyond $16k\Omega$ or so, the higher frequencies start to get choked and the output falls away. Pickups with a resistance of $6 - 12k\Omega$ are referred to as high impedance, while anything below $1k\Omega$ is considered low impedance.

Many of the early pickups made by manufacturers such as Fender and Gibson, were hand traversed. This meant that although the coils were wound on a machine, the actual winding process was guided by an operator, and would occasionally be uneven. Most of the time this made little difference, but occasionally a pickup would be produced with a unique and distinctive tone. Today these pickups are very sought after, especially original Gibson PAFs. Unfortunately though, just putting an old PAF into a new guitar will not guarantee a wonderful tone. There are too many variables involved that might possibly affect its sound, from its exact positioning under the strings, to the chemical composition of the lacquer used to seal it when it was made. Intangible factors like these can make some old pickups sound amazing, and others mediocre.

Humbucking Pickups

The pickups we have looked at so far have been the single coil variety. Because coils tend to act like 'aerials' when connected to high gain guitar amps, care has to be taken to ensure that they are well screened and have good earth connections. Failure to pay attention to this can lead to noise problems. It is surprising how much quieter in terms of noise a well screened guitar can be (see section on noise reduction).

Until the mid 1950s there was no alternative to the single coil pickup, and guitarists had to put up with the interference from radio stations and stray magnetic fields that their instruments attracted. Then in 1956 the Gibson company produced a pickup that combined two coils connected out of phase so that they cancelled out all signals except direct disruptions of the magnetic field (Fig.1.5). This type of pickup combines a high output with very low noise levels.

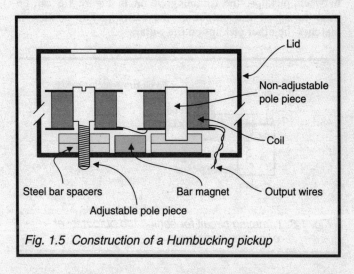

Fig. 1.5 Construction of a Humbucking pickup

Humbuckers can share a single bar magnet split between the two coils, with magnetised slugs acting as pole pieces. Or they may have twelve separate magnets and be similar to a couple of single coil pickups mounted side by side. One set of six slugs are often adjustable.

The two coils in a humbucker are usually connected in series, but may also be wired in parallel to produce a more delicate sound (see guitar circuits).

Active Pickups

An active pickup is simply a pickup with a built in preamp to give it a greater output. They are available as replacements for all the common styles of guitar and bass pickup, and can usually be fitted without too much trouble, the only extra components required being a battery to power the preamp, and some form of on/off switch.

A problem that may be encountered when mixing passive and active pickups on the same instrument, is the balancing of their relative output levels — an active humbucker might well be somewhat louder than a passive single coil unit. If you want to avoid having to reset the volume when you switch between pickups, the trimming circuit in Figure 1.6 can be used to adjust the output of the active pickup so that it matches the other pickups on the guitar.

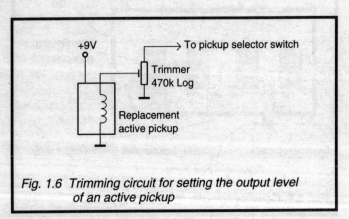

Fig. 1.6 Trimming circuit for setting the output level of an active pickup

Piezo-electric Pickups

Piezo pickups rely on the fact that certain crystalline substances produce a current when subjected to pressure. The greater the pressure, the higher the current. A piezo pickup consists simply of a ceramic crystal sandwiched between two

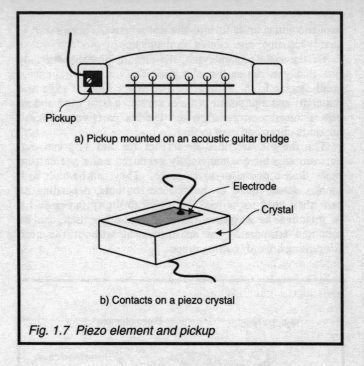

Pickup

a) Pickup mounted on an acoustic guitar bridge

Electrode

Crystal

b) Contacts on a piezo crystal

Fig. 1.7 Piezo element and pickup

electrodes (Fig.1.7). This can be set in resin and mounted in an area of high vibration such as the bridge of an acoustic guitar. Piezos can produce an extremely high quality signal if used correctly, the only drawback with them tends to be that they have a low output, and usually need a preamp before they can drive a normal instrument amplifier.

Making a Piezo Pickup

Piezo contact pickups are extremely versatile sound trans-ducers. They can be mounted on virtually any surface, letting you amplify old or valuable instruments without needing to modify them. There are a number of different piezo pickup designs to fit various groups of instruments. They generally mount on or near to the bridge because this is the area of highest vibration. Complete violin and double bass bridges are available that have a transducer built in, and some acoustic guitar units fit into the slot where the bridge rests so that it actually presses down on the pickup.

Of the main pickup types, the piezo is probably the only one that you can realistically build for yourself, and expect good results from, without having to get hold of expensive materials and equipment — there are no coils to wind and no critical measurements involved. The few parts you will need are quite cheap and easy to find.

The designs described here (Figs 1.8 and 1.9) can out-perform expensive commercially produced units, yet cost no more than a pound or so to make. They can be built with mono, stereo, quad or hexaphonic outputs, depending on how they need to be used. The pickup shown in Figure 1.8 is intended as a general purpose transducer that can be mounted temporarily on an instrument without the need for drilling holes or cutting routs.

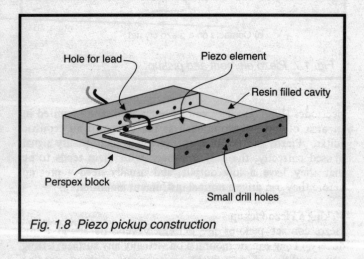

Fig. 1.8 Piezo pickup construction

I have found that pickups like this, made with two piezo elements, are versatile enough for acoustic guitars in most situations, but if you need more complex control, perhaps for recording, you may want to have extra outputs to give an expanded balance.

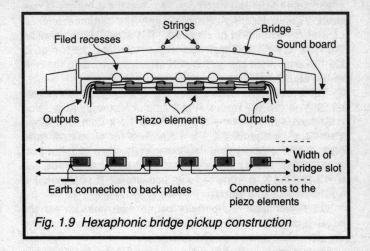

Fig. 1.9 Hexaphonic bridge pickup construction

Figure 1.9 is a more specialised pickup for fitting underneath the bridge of an acoustic guitar with the strings pressing
down on it, and has a separate output for each string.

Many commercially available bridge pickups only have one
output, even if individual crystal elements are utilised for each
string. This can make the pickup troublesome to set up,
because if the bridge is not absolutely flat, uneven string
pressure will make some strings sound louder than others.

To build a general purpose piezo pickup you will need a
small piece of Perspex or other hard plastic, a 40mm piezo
transducer element, a short length of thin screened wire, and
some epoxy resin (potting compound or fibre glass resin will
do).

Start by cutting the round piezo element into quarters with
a pair of tin snips. On some larger elements the brass plates
are quite thick, which makes this difficult. You may need
to grind some of the crystal away before you cut, to stop it
cracking at the edges. A small hobby drill with a flat grinding
wheel is ideal for doing this. The most important thing here
is to get a flat piece with the top silvering intact, and enough
metal at the side to solder to.

Next, strip back and tin the screened wire so that it can be
soldered to the element. It is quite difficult to get a good

connection to the top silvered surface because it burns off very easily. To avoid this you should apply the minimum amount of heat for a fraction of a second. Put a small blob of solder onto the crystal and melt the tinned wire into the top of it. Do the same with the screen wire which connects to the edge of the brass base plate.

The transducer case is made from a small piece of Perspex, which you can get from a model shop or hardware store. You only need a tiny piece — approx. $0.5 \times 1.5 \times 2$cm for a mono transducer, and around $0.5 \times 1.5 \times 5$cm for a stereo or quad unit. These measurements are completely up to you, but bear in mind that if it's much smaller it will have a low output, and if it's too big it is liable to look incongruous if you mount it on the outside of a guitar.

Once you have the perspex cut to size, you can get the edges square by rubbing them on a piece of 240 grade wet and dry paper laid down on a flat surface.

With a small hacksaw, cut a couple of slots about halfway down the block and remove the material from the middle by drilling or filing it away. You should end up with a shape roughly like the diagram. The slot needs to be wide enough to mount one of the small piezo elements, and deep enough to allow for its solder connections.

Drill a hole of the same diameter as the lead wire in the side of the block so that it meets up with the bottom of the main slot, and make several smaller holes along the sides — these clog with resin when the case is filled and hold the whole thing together. Thread the lead through until the element is positioned in the slot, and once in place, use super glue to hold it down. The next stage is to fill the case with epoxy resin so that you end up with a solid plastic block. Stick the transducer down on a flat surface and cover the ends with tape to form a mould for the resin. Spray a little WD40 or light oil over the inside of the case so that the resin will not actually stick to the transducer element or the inside of the slot. I have found that doing this seems to increase the effectiveness of the pickup, probably by allowing vibrations to affect the crystal more easily. The hard resin will be held in place by the small side holes. It's a good idea to test the transducer at this point because once it is full of resin there is very little you can do to it. Connect the lead to the input of an amplifier and check that you get a signal when you tap the transducer.

If everything is working, mix up a little resin, and fill the slot until the element is covered over.

Once the resin is set you can remove the tape and clean up the edges with wet and dry paper. If the transducer is going on the outside of a guitar, it can be sprayed with matt acrylic paint to make it look more professional.

For a stereo transducer you need to mount two separate crystal elements, one at either end of the case. They can be wired to share a common earth, or have totally isolated outputs, which may be useful if you want to change their relative polarity. Piezo elements can be connected in series or parallel.

For quad and hexaphonic pickups you simply use four or six elements and split them up into a number of output combinations.

When deciding where to mount the pickup on a guitar you should stick it down temporarily with double-sided tape. Do not hold the pickup with your fingers as this will give a false impression of the sound it is likely to produce. The bridge area is usually the best place to start. You may find that one side of the transducer has a higher output than the other, so you will need to experiment.

For more permanent fixing, on the inside of the sound board for example, use an epoxy glue such as Araldite. If you have made a stereo pickup, mount it along the back of the bridge so that one element is near the top strings and the other near the bass. This will make it easier to get a good balance between the strings.

Hexaphonic Pickup

A hexaphonic bridge pickup (Fig.1.9) is a little more difficult to assemble because it has to be very small and thin to fit into the bridge slot without making the bridge too high.

The advantage of having a pickup right under the bridge is that the string vibrations are transmitted directly to it and are therefore at their strongest.

To make a hexaphonic pickup, first measure the size of the slot where the bridge rests. It may be difficult to prise the bridge saddle out, so be careful not to damage the surrounding wood. If the slot is very shallow you may not have enough room for a pickup without routing it deeper, or sanding some material from the bottom of the bridge. The finished pickup will be at least 2mm high, and can be made from one medium sized piezo disc.

Once you know how wide the bridge slot is, pieces of piezo crystal can be cut to fit inside. Because the individual transducers for each string will have to be quite small, it is best to get a piezo disc with a thin backing plate. This will enable narrow slices to be cut using tin snips. Try to keep the crystal from breaking away from the metal. You will need six pieces of crystal, one for each string, measuring about 5mm × 3mm — or slightly smaller than the width of the bridge slot.

When you have the elements cut, check that they will fit lined up in the bridge slot, with each string having an element directly underneath it. Then take the elements and place on a flat surface, face down in the same position. Solder a fine wire along the sides of the backing plates to connect them together (Fig.1.9).

This wire acts as the common earth and will also hold everything in position while the pickup is being constructed. Remember to make all the solder connections as small as possible to keep the height down. It is best to tin the wire and the metal with a small amount of solder, then just melt the connection together. Once the earth wire has been connected, turn the pickup over and solder a fine enamelled wire to the silvered side of each element. These wires are the output connections and should be positioned so that they don't short with any of the other elements. When the fine wires are in place they can be taken to the ends of the assembly and soldered to thicker leads.

In order to have the pickup in a suitable state for mounting in the bridge, it needs to be set in resin. You can make a resin mould out of thick card and tape.

When filling the mould, position the pickup assembly with the earth plates facing upwards and the output leads emerging from the bottom, then pour the resin into the mould in thin layers until the six earth plates are covered. You may wish to stick clear tape over the tops of the crystals first, to keep the resin from coming into contact with every surface of the element.

Once the resin is hard the pickup can be squared up with 400 grade wet and dry paper. Be careful not to break the output wires when doing this.

When the pickup is ready to fit to the guitar, drill two small holes at either end of the bridge slot for the output wires to go through. The pickup should be a fairly loose fit in the slot, with the bridge holding it in place.

Having the pickup underneath it will probably make the bridge too high. The height can be altered by removing material from the bottom of the saddle. Remember to keep this edge as flat as possible to ensure that the pickup is held down along its whole length when the strings are in place.

When using a hexaphonic pickup there may be some degree of crosstalk between adjacent elements. This can be reduced by filing away the bottom of the bridge saddle so that only the parts directly over the elements are in contact with the pickup. Be careful not to take too much material away if you do this, as it may weaken the bridge. The corresponding areas between the piezo elements in the pickup can also be filed away.

Piezo Preamp

Because the signal outputs from piezo transducers are generally quite low, they can usually do with a preamp to boost them up to a reasonable level. Having a preamp also helps if you want to use an EQ to straighten out any strange resonant peaks that your set up may have.

Figure 1.10 shows a simple single transistor preamp for boosting piezo pickups. It is based around a 2N3819 general purpose FET, in common source mode. FETs are often used for this type of small signal application because they have a high input impedance and can offer good noise performance.

Signals from the transducer reach Tr1 via the input capacitor C1 with R1 setting the gate bias. C2 is connected across the input to help limit any high frequency interference that may occur. C3 and C5 act as decoupling capacitors.

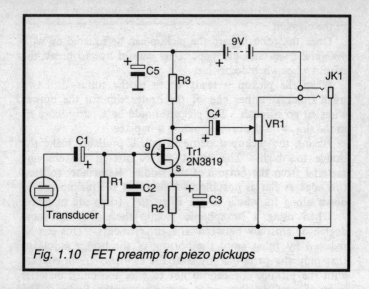

Fig. 1.10   FET preamp for piezo pickups

Six-channel Piezo Preamp/Mixer

To get the best results from multiple output or under the bridge type pickup, it is helpful to have an independent level control for each string so that their relative loudness can be balanced.   Figure 1.11 shows a six-channel preamp/mixer that enables the output from each string to be adjusted.   The pre-amp circuitry for each channel is basically the same as the single unit shown in Figure 1.10, with the outputs from each of the six elements fed to a passive mixer made up from VR1 – VR6.   These presets can be mounted with the preamps inside the guitar as they will not need much attention after an initial set-up.   Preset VR7 controls the overall output level of the circuit.

Three-band Equaliser

Figure 1.12 shows a simple three band passive equaliser that can be connected to the output of a guitar preamp.   The circuit could be used on its own, if the output of the guitar is strong enough, but will be less effective without a preamp because it reduces the level of signals passing through it.

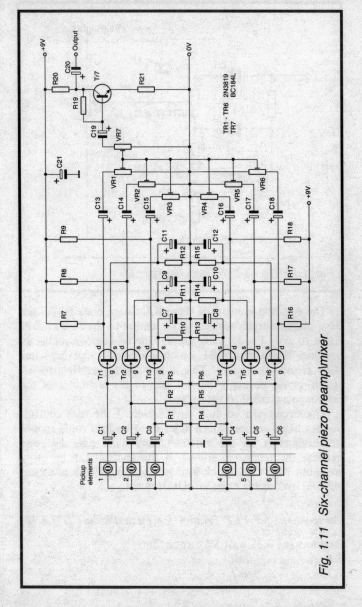

Fig. 1.11 Six-channel piezo preamp\mixer

17

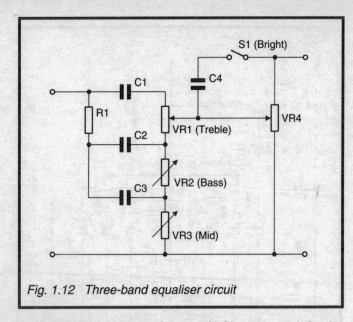

Fig. 1.12 Three-band equaliser circuit

The equaliser consists of three R/C filters, one each for the bass, mid and treble ranges, and is similar to the tone circuits fitted to early Fender valve amps. The volume control has an optional 'bright' switch S1, which connects a 150pF capacitor (C4) across the wiper. This allows the higher frequencies, which would normally be lost due to the resistance of the pot, to pass straight to the output.

The circuit can be built with presets if the tone controls are not likely to need much adjustment, or you could mount potentiometers on the guitar. Small slider pots are good because the relative positions of the controls can be easily seen, but have a drawback in that they are difficult to mount without making big holes in an instrument.

Components for FET Preamp for Piezo Pickups (Fig.1.10)

Resistors (all 0.25 watt 5% carbon film)
R1   2M2
R2   4k7

18

| R3 | 2k7 |
| VR1 | 470k log potentiometer (optional) |

Capacitors

C1, C4	1μF 16V tantalum bead
C2	39pF ceramic disc
C3	4μ7F 16V electrolytic
C5	47μF 16V electrolytic

Semiconductors

| Tr1 | 2N3819 general purpose FET |

Miscellaneous

Stereo jack socket
PP3 9V battery

Components for Six-channel Piezo Preamp/mixer (Fig.1.11)

Resistors (all 0.25 watt 5% carbon film)

R1 – R6	2M2
R7 – R9, &	
R16 – R18	2k7
R10 – R15	4k7
R19	1M
R20	3k3
R21	820R
VR1 – VR7	100k log preset potentiometers

Capacitors

C1 – C6, &	
C13 – C20	1μF tantalum 16V
C7 – C12	4μ7 electrolytic 16V
C21	100μF electrolytic

Semiconductors

| Tr1 – Tr6 | 2N3819 FET |
| Tr7 | BC184L |

Components for Three-band Equaliser (Fig.1.12)

Resistors (all 0.25 watt 5% carbon film)
R1	10k
VR1	220k lin potentiometer
VR2	220k lin potentiometer
VR3	10k lin potentiometer
VR4	470k log potentiometer

Capacitors
C1	220pF polystyrene
C2	100nF polyester
C3	47nF polyester
C4	150pF polystyrene

Miscellaneous
S1	SPST mini toggle switch

Acoustic Guitar Microphone

If you need to amplify an acoustic guitar and want to use a
microphone instead of, or as well as, a pickup, the microphone
usually needs to be positioned near to the sound hole for the
most effective sound. Playing into a microphone is OK if you
don't plan to move about much, but on stage it can be a bit
of a limitation. One way round this is to have the microphone, or the mic element at least, mounted inside the guitar.
There are commercially available guitar mics designed to be
used in this way, but it is quite easy to construct your own
system without having to do much modification.

Mounting a mic inside a guitar can cause a couple of
problems. The biggest one is likely to be acoustic feedback.
This can be overcome to a large extent by positioning the
microphone carefully, and paying attention to volume settings.
An equaliser circuit is also helpful, to limit the resonant frequencies at which feedback occurs. The other problem that
might affect the performance of an internal mic is that of
vibrations reaching it via its mounting. The ideal way for a mic
to be mounted would be hovering, free from anything that
could transmit vibrations to it physically, but as this isn't

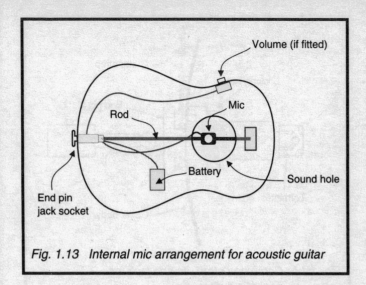

Fig. 1.13   Internal mic arrangement for acoustic guitar

practical inside a guitar, the next best thing is to make sure that the mounting or holder is well damped, that is, made from materials which don't readily transmit vibrations.

The internal mic arrangement shown in Figure 1.13 employs an omnidirectional sub-miniature condenser mic element mounted on a thin metal rod which runs the length of the guitar body. This allows for a reasonable amount of position adjustment, yet holds the mic firmly.

The rod is attached at the back of the guitar to a combined end pin and 1/4in stereo output jack (Fig.1.14). You can get these from most music shops. They enable a normal guitar lead to be used with the guitar.

The construction of the mic holder is quite straightforward. A small plastic potting box can be used. Drill a hole low down in either side, big enough to slide the rod in, and another smaller hole for the mic lead (Fig.1.15).

To keep the risk of vibration down to a minimum the wires that go to the mic element need to be quite thin. They can be soldered to a couple of tags, and attached to the inside of the potting box, where a thicker screened cable may be connected, to take the signal to the end pin jack.

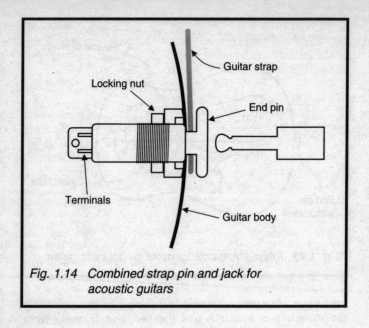

Fig. 1.14 Combined strap pin and jack for acoustic guitars

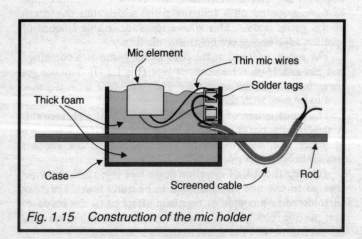

Fig. 1.15 Construction of the mic holder

In order that the mic holder is free to move on the mounting rod, yet remains static once it has been positioned, the lower part of the potting box can be packed with plastic foam. This will press up on the rod and keep it tight.

The mic element should be placed facing upwards above the rod, held in place by a similar soft foam.

Fitting a combined jack and end pin will require a hole of approximately 12mm to be drilled where the normal rear strap pin is located. The exact size of this hole will depend on the type of socket used. Having a large hole for the jack is useful as it allows the mounting rod to be pushed in from the back of the guitar. The rod should first be securely attached to the earth terminal of the end pin, which serves as a good anchor point.

The mic holder can be pushed into place and wired up once the rod is inside the guitar. If the rod isn't stiff enough with only one mounting, the other end may be attached to the inside of the guitar using a small wooden spacer.

The quality of the microphone element that you use is obviously important if you are going to achieve a decent sound.

The small condenser mic elements described here are relatively cheap, and produce surprisingly good results, even though they have a frequency response with an upper limit of around 8kHz. This type of microphone has a built in FET preamp and requires a 1.5V power supply, a decoupling capacitor, and a resistor (Fig.1.16).

The 1.5V can be easily provided by a battery mounted inside the guitar. Even with constant use, a normal dry battery should last several months.

If an onboard preamp is to be used with the mic, perhaps as part of a combined piezo/mic arrangement, the limiting resistor can be increased to 15k and the mic connected to a 9V supply.

Other types of microphone element such as dynamic or moving coil, will not require a battery or the additional components needed for the electret mics. They can have their signals taken straight to the output jack. Figures 1.17 and 1.18 show set-ups for using both a piezo transducer and an internal mic. The first circuit employs a moving coil mic

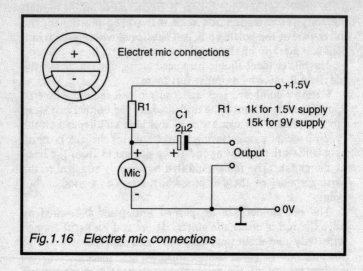

Fig.1.16 Electret mic connections

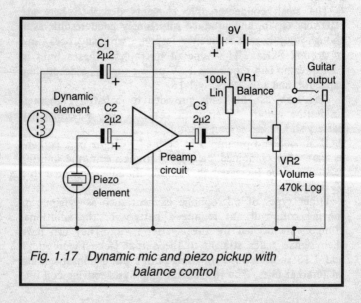

Fig. 1.17 Dynamic mic and piezo pickup with balance control

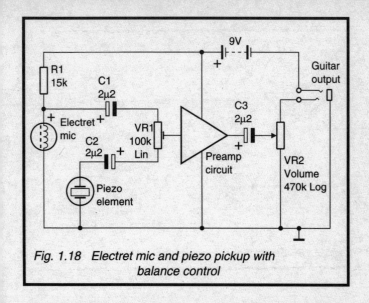

Fig. 1.18 Electret mic and piezo pickup with balance control

element which requires no power supply. The second has an electret mic sharing the power supply of the piezo preamp. In both circuits the preset VR1 acts as a balance control to enable the relative volumes of the two transducers to be set.

Chapter 2

GUITAR CIRCUITRY

In this section we will look at some common guitar circuits, and ways in which they can be modified. These circuits represent the type of thing likely to be found in 90% of instruments, and should enable you to understand the basic building blocks needed to create your own custom designs.

Switches

The switches for selecting the pickup combinations on electric guitars are generally one of two types. On Fender style instruments, including most 3-pickup, and Japanese or Korean copies, three or five position slider switches are used. Older guitars tend to have the three position variety which allows only one pickup to be selected at a time. The five position switches that came in later enable combinations of bridge/middle and middle/neck pickups to be used as well. The switches themselves are dual 3 or 5 way single pole, and as both types have the same contact layout, they can easily be exchanged for one another (Fig.2.1).

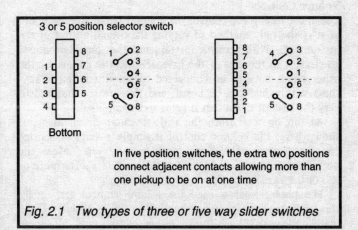

Fig. 2.1   Two types of three or five way slider switches

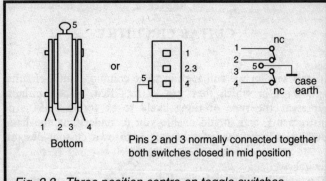

Fig. 2.2   Three position centre-on toggle switches

The other type of specialised pickup selector, commonly found on 2-pickup guitars, is a three way centre-on switch which allows each pickup to be connected separately, or both together (Fig.2.2).

Normal SPST or DPDT toggle and slide switches are sometimes used for pickup selection, as they can allow for greater flexibility and the inclusion of other functions such as coil taps and phase reversal.

Volume Controls

The most important control on a guitar is the volume knob, as it is the only method of varying the overall output of the instrument. With acoustic instruments, the sounds produced go straight to the ears of the listener. Electric guitars, on the other hand, have to be connected to amplifiers before anything worthwhile can be heard, and this creates the need to vary the level of signal that is going to be amplified.

As can be seen from the various guitar circuit diagrams shown here, the volume control is simply a variable resistor connected across the signal path, usually just before the output of the guitar. In action, the control shorts more or less of the signal to earth.

The potentiometers used for volume control are usually the logarithmic type, sometimes called 'audio taper'. These match the ears' logarithmic response to sound. If linear potentiometers are fitted, they tend to sound uneven, with little effect until the last few degrees of travel, when there is a sudden increase in volume.

Tone Controls

Along with the volume control, a tone control circuit is usually included on an electric guitar. A very basic arrangement is often used, based around a resistor and capacitor forming a low pass filter. This is connected across the signal path, usually ahead of the volume control, and allows the treble frequencies to be progressively bled to earth.

The variable element in these circuits is invariably a potentiometer connected in series with the other components, though in more complicated circuits there are sometimes a number of different value capacitors selected by a multi-way switch.

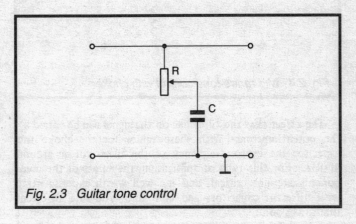

Fig. 2.3   Guitar tone control

Figure 2.3 shows the type of passive tone control found on the majority of instruments. The action of the circuit is fairly limited, especially in guitars that have less than desirable pickups. Often, turning down a tone control will simply reduce the small amount of signal clarity that was there to start off with and produce a muddy, undefined sound.

The value of capacitor used for these simple tone controls range from about 0.01 to 0.05μF with potentiometer values of

100 – 500k. As well as R/C filters, there are designs that use coil/capacitor combinations to provide mid range tone controls. Circuits like this can be quite effective in providing a greater variation of usable sounds, though they tend to appear only on more expensive instruments. Figure 2.4 is a mid range tone circuit that can be connected in parallel with an existing tone control. It uses a 1.5H audio choke and a 0.01μF capacitor to form a passive band pass filter.

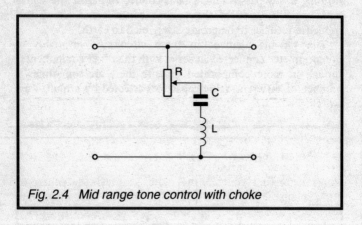

Fig. 2.4   Mid range tone control with choke

The effect that the filter has on the signal can be varied by the potentiometer. With these values for the choke and capacitor the centre frequency of the filter will be around 400Hz. For this type of application, the values of the components are not critical, and it's well worth experimenting with different capacitors and coils until you find an effect that suits you.

Figure 2.5 is a six position tone control that can be fitted on its own to replace a tone control, or used to augment an existing circuit. This arrangement was used on some Gibson guitars and is known as a 'varitone'. The circuit can be situated after the volume control, or after the pickup depending on the layout of the guitar. It employs a six position rotary switch to connect any one of five different value capacitors in series with a 1.5H choke. Series resistors are also included to balance the circuit, with the first switch

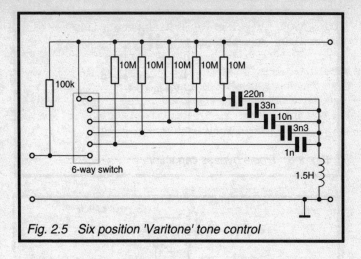

Fig. 2.5 Six position 'Varitone' tone control

position acting as a filter bypass. The capacitor values shown give a smooth progressive action but are not critical.

Volume Bypass Capacitor
When the volume control on a guitar is turned down there is often a slight, but noticeable drop in the high frequency content of the signal. This is probably why electric guitars sound much better when you play them with the volume turned right up. Some players fit switches across the volume control so that there is nothing between the pickup and the amplifier to dampen the signal. The idea behind this is that even when the control is fully open, the resistance across the pickup will be effecting its output. I've found the fitting of volume bypass switches a little subjective, but a lot of people really believe they improve their sound.

A way to get round the problem of treble loss at low volume is to connect a bypass capacitor across the input and output of the volume pot. If you play a Telecaster, you will already have one of these capacitors fitted, some other guitars have them as well. All they do is let the high frequencies through to the output regardless of how the volume control is set. Because the capacitor is only small (around $0.001\mu F$) it does not affect the normal action of the volume

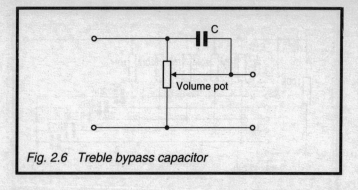

Fig. 2.6   Treble bypass capacitor

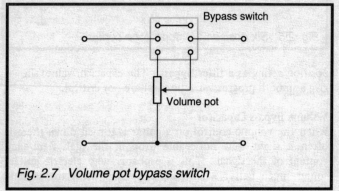

Fig. 2.7   Volume pot bypass switch

control.

Figures 2.6 and 2.7 show how to connect a treble bypass capacitor and a volume bypass switch.

Pull Pots

To cut down on the number of external controls needed to give the various switching options that might be included on a guitar, a combined potentiometer and switch called a 'pull pot' (Fig.2.8) is sometimes used. A pull pot can take the place of a volume or tone control potentiometer without the need to drill any extra holes in an instrument. From the outside of the guitar a pull pot looks exactly like a normal control, but by pulling the shaft out slightly, a switch is operated underneath

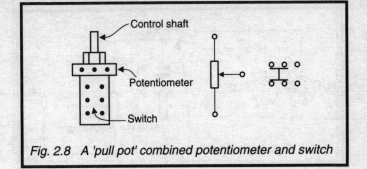

Fig. 2.8   A 'pull pot' combined potentiometer and switch

the potentiometer. The types of switch generally available in this format seems to be limited to DPDT and SPST, though you may occasionally come across custom designs on some guitars.

Circuits

Figure 2.9 shows a basic circuit for an electric guitar or bass. It has one single coil pickup, a volume control, and a tone control. This arrangement has been used on many instruments, though the component values can vary. It could be further simplified by omission of the tone control components. The single coil pickup could also easily be replaced by a twin coil unit.

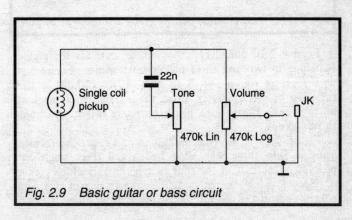

Fig. 2.9   Basic guitar or bass circuit

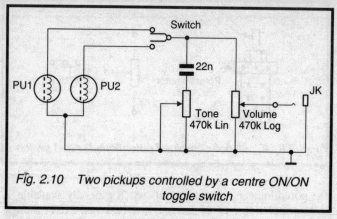

Fig. 2.10   Two pickups controlled by a centre ON/ON toggle switch

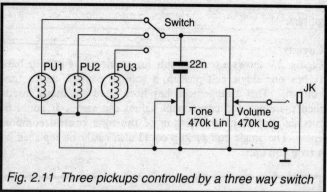

Fig. 2.11 Three pickups controlled by a three way switch

Figures 2.10 and 2.11 show simple methods for pickup switching in two and three pickup instruments. Figure 2.10 uses a centre on/on switch to control two pickups so that they can be on separately, or in the middle switch position, on together. Figure 2.11 has a three way switch controlling three pickups.

Figure 2.12 is the basic circuit for a Fender Stratocaster using a twin three way slide switch and three single coil pickups. One half of the slide switch controls which pickup is selected, while the other half connects one of two tone controls across the output. This arrangement allows the neck

34

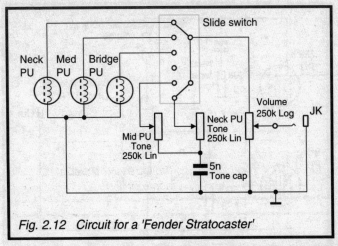

Fig. 2.12   Circuit for a 'Fender Stratocaster'

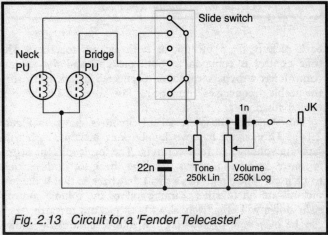

Fig. 2.13   Circuit for a 'Fender Telecaster'

and middle pickups to have their tone controls pre-set, with both controls sharing the same capacitor. The bridge pickup has no tone control, and a single volume control governs the overall output of the instrument.

Figure 2.13 shows the usual arrangement for a twin single coil pickup Telecaster. This circuit is simpler than the Stratocaster but uses the same type of slide switch to turn on the

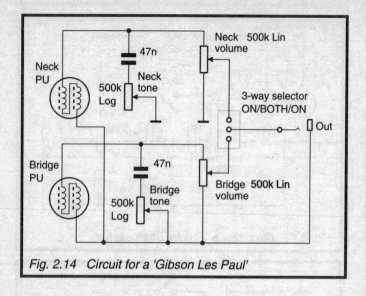

Fig. 2.14   Circuit for a 'Gibson Les Paul'

back pickup, front pickup, or both pickups together. The tone control is common to both pickups, and the volume control has a bypass capacitor connected across it to stop the treble frequencies from being lost when the volume is turned down.

The standard Gibson Les Paul circuit is shown in Figure 2.14. This circuit has two humbucking pickups, each with separate volume and tone controls. The toggle selector switch is centre on/on and allows the front, back, or both pickups to be used. The circuit has a slight drawback in that if the two pickups are on together, turning one of the volume controls right down will effectively short both pickups to earth. This can be overcome by rewiring the volume controls as shown in Figure 2.15.

Figures 2.16 to 2.22 are examples of how to connect various pickup switching systems.

Figure 2.16 is a simple but versatile way of controlling three pickups using three SPST switches. This kind of arrangement is used quite a lot on strat style guitars, and allows any combination of pickups to be selected.

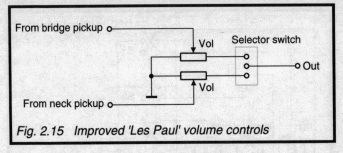

Fig. 2.15 Improved 'Les Paul' volume controls

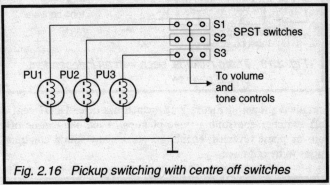

Fig. 2.16 Pickup switching with centre off switches

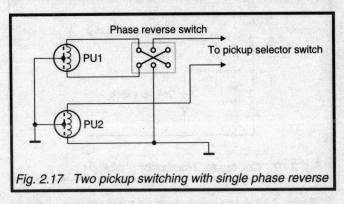

Fig. 2.17 Two pickup switching with single phase reverse

The circuit in Figure 2.17 is a two pickup circuit that uses a DPDT switch to enable one pickup to have its phase reversed in relation to the other. A more complicated phase switching

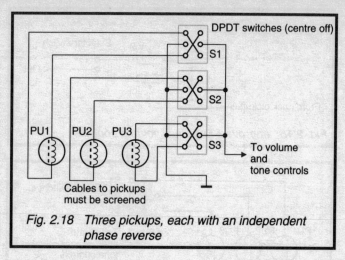

Fig. 2.18   Three pickups, each with an independent phase reverse

circuit is shown in Figure 2.18, which has three DPDT centre off switches controlling three pickups. Each one can be off, on, or phase reversed, enabling a great many sound combinations to be obtained.

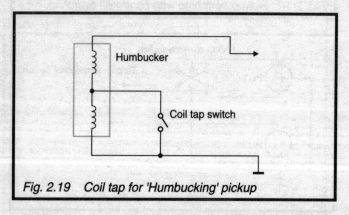

Fig. 2.19   Coil tap for 'Humbucking' pickup

Figure 2.19 shows how to connect a coil tap to a humbucking pickup. It is usual to have the coil with non-adjustable poles shorted by the switch. If you have a humbucker with only two wires, it is often possible to remove the case and make a connection for a coil tap where the two coils are joined. The coils can also be split and given separate output wires.

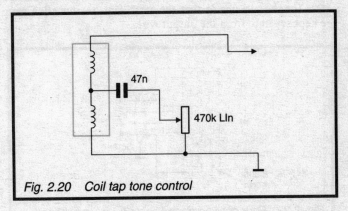

Fig. 2.20   Coil tap tone control

Figure 2.20 is a coil tap used as a tone control. This is quite effective if you want to mix a single coil and humbucking sound without adding an extra switch.

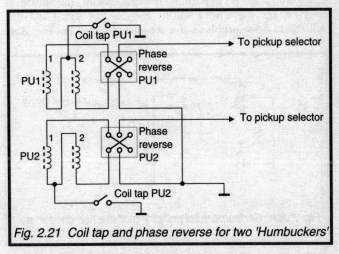

Fig. 2.21 Coil tap and phase reverse for two 'Humbuckers'

Figure 2.21 is great if you want a really versatile twin humbucker guitar. It has a coil tap and phase reverse for each

39

pickup, and can easily be constructed using pull pots if the guitar has two volume and tone controls. When you build circuits with phase reversal switches, use multi core screened cable for the pickups so that the earth screen connection can be kept separate from the output wires.

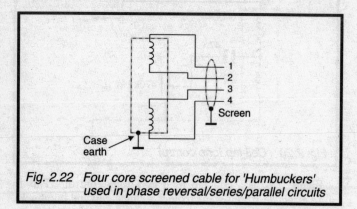

Fig. 2.22   Four core screened cable for 'Humbuckers' used in phase reversal/series/parallel circuits

Figure 2.22 is important because, when the phase is reversed, the earth wire will be carrying the signal and this will create noise problems if a separate screen is not included.

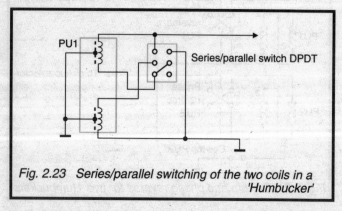

Fig. 2.23   Series/parallel switching of the two coils in a 'Humbucker'

A humbucking pickup can have its coils connected in both series and parallel to create different effects. Figure 2.23

shows how to wire a DPDT switch to give both options. As with other circuits that require both coils to have independent outputs, the cable to the changeover switch must have a separate earth. This circuit can also be used with a couple of single coil pickups.

Chapter 3

ACTIVE CIRCUITS

Electric Guitar Preamp

Although electric guitars are designed to drive amplifiers directly, it can be an advantage for an instrument to have more output power, especially if it has weak or thin sounding pickups. As with the piezo preamp, having more power available can improve the action of passive tone controls, and feeding a guitar amp with a signal that is already at a high level gives you the option of overdriving the input stage. This is not normally desirable with acoustic instruments, but is great for giving more bite to electric guitars.

Figure 3.1 is a variable gain preamp that can be connected to the pickup, or to the selector switch, if a guitar has more than one pickup.

It is based around a low noise TLO71 wired as an inverting amplifier with the gain controlled by VR1. R3 acts as an endstop so that at minimum setting the gain of the circuit is unity. A bypass switch is included, as well as normal passive tone and volume controls. These still operate in the usual way when the circuit is bypassed.

Using the component values shown, the voltage gain of the circuit (VR1+R3/R1) can be varied from unity to around 10, which should be more than enough for most applications. If the preamp is just going to be used as a simple volume boost you could have a preset for VR1 and use the switch to bring the circuit in when you need it.

The circuit has a wide frequency response and will work equally well with bass guitars.

Components for Low Noise Electric Guitar Preamp (Fig.3.1)

Resistors (all 0.25 watt 5% carbon film)

R1 – R4	47k
VR1	470k log preset potentiometer
VR2	470k log potentiometer
VR3	470k lin potentiometer

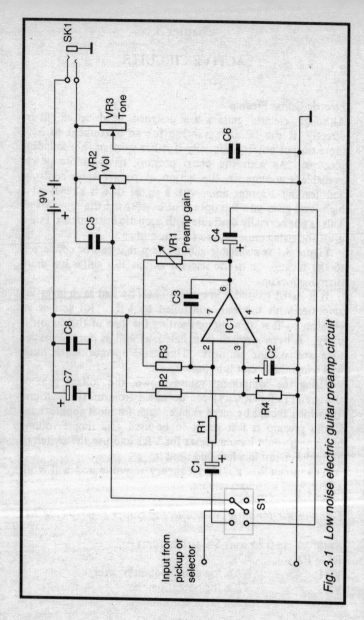

Fig. 3.1 Low noise electric guitar preamp circuit

44

Capacitors

C1, C2, C4	1μF 16V tantalum
C3	39pF ceramic disk
C5	1nF ceramic disk
C6	22nF polyester
C7	10μF 16V tantalum
C8	100nF polyester

Semiconductors

IC1	TLO71 low noise op-amp

Miscellaneous

S1	DPDT mini toggle switch
SK1	stereo jack socket
PP3	9V battery

Tone Boosters

One of the simplest active circuits you can build into a guitar is a treble booster, which you can use to improve high frequency response. The circuit shown in Figure 3.2 is an active high pass filter. The gain of the circuit can be set by VR2 so that it matches the normal guitar signal level. VR1 controls the range of the effect by allowing more or less of the high frequency content of the signal to be fed back to the input.

The booster can be connected in place of the normal guitar tone circuit, or if it needs to be switched in and out, a stereo pot could be utilised as both an active and passive control. A DPDT switch will be needed to bypass the circuit.

The treble booster can be built using the PCB layout shown in Figure 3.3. This board has both presets mounted on it, and should be small enough to fit inside most guitars. If a stereo jack is going to be used as the power switch, the extra pads A and B can be utilised for connecting the negative battery wire to the switch terminal. Figure 3.4 shows the component overlay.

Components for Treble Booster (Fig.3.2)

Resistors (all 0.25 watt 5% carbon film)

R1	330k
R2	2k2

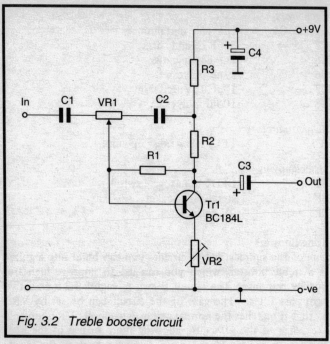

Fig. 3.2   Treble booster circuit

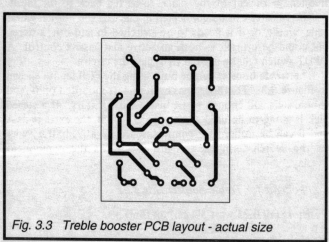

Fig. 3.3   Treble booster PCB layout - actual size

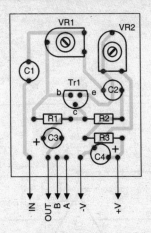

Fig. 3.4   Treble booster components overlay

R3	1k
VR1	100k lin preset potentiometer
VR2	4k7 lin preset potentiometer

Capacitors

C1, C2	1n2 ceramic disc
C3	1μF 16V electrolytic
C4	10μF 16V electrolytic

Semiconductors

Tr1	BC184L low noise NPN

Mid Range Booster

If you need a mid range booster, you can build a band pass filter into the feedback loop of an op amp.

A band pass filter with a sharp resonant peak will produce the familiar wah wah effect if its pass band is swept up and down the audio spectrum. The circuit shown in Figure 3.5 could be used as a wah wah by making VR3 continuously variable, but is really intended as a preset unit that can be switched in and out to boost selected frequencies for solos, etc.

47

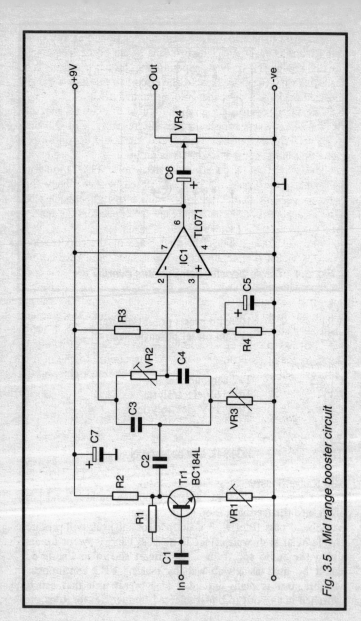

Fig. 3.5 Mid range booster circuit

48

The pass band of the filter can be positioned at any point in the audio spectrum, which means it can boost frequencies in the treble, mid or bass, depending on how it is set up. You can also vary the resonance of the circuit to produce a sharply defined peak, or a smoother, more rounded effect.

The filter requires a minimum number of external controls. If you use pre-sets for all the variable resistors, you will only need a DPDT switch as a bypass, and this could be built into a tone or volume control if you use a pull-pot.

The circuit is based around a low noise TLO71 op-amp.

Signals enter via C1 and are buffered by Tr1. They then pass to IC1 which has the filter built into its feedback path. The important components here are the capacitors C3 and C4, and the presets VR2 and VR3.

VR1 sets the gain for the first stage of the circuit and is used to match the pickup to the input. VR2 and VR3 control the resonance of the filter, and the position of the pass band in the audio spectrum.

When setting the circuit up use VR1 to limit the output from the pickup so that it is not overloading the filter and causing distortion — unless you want distortion — then adjust the settings of the filter with VR2 and VR3. VR4 can be used to match the output level of the circuit to the normal unprocessed guitar sound so that there is the right amount of overall level boost.

Components for Mid Range Booster (Fig.3.5)

Resistors (all 0.25 watt 5% carbon film)
R1	560k
R2	3k3
R3, R4	100k
VR1	4k7 lin preset potentiometer
VR2	470k log preset potentiometer
VR3	10k lin preset potentiometer
VR4	100k log preset potentiometer

Capacitors
C1 — C4	0.1µF polyester
C5	10µF 16V electrolytic

| C6 | 1μF 16V electrolytic |
| C7 | 100μF 16V electrolytic |

Semiconductors

| Tr1 | BC184L low noise NPN transistor |
| IC1 | TLO71 low noise op-amp |

Active Tone Control

If you need more versatility from the tone controls on an instrument than can be obtained with conventional passive filters, you might like to consider using active circuitry. Active tone circuits can really improve the performance of a guitar because they allow you to boost areas of a signal as well as cut them. This gives you many more tonal colours.

The active tone shown in Figure 3.6 has two controls. One for the bass and one for the treble. It was intended as an on-board unit, but could also be used as an external effect. This type of circuit was originally designed by Peter Baxandall, and is found extensively in audio amplifiers. It gives about 20dB of cut and boost over both frequency ranges and also has the advantage of being reasonably quiet.

Circuit

The active tone control is built around a TLO72 dual op-amp, which gives a good level of noise performance, and is still relatively cheap. An ultra low noise IC like the 4227G could be used, but at this level of design it is unlikely that any big improvement would be noticed.

Signals enter the circuit via C1 and are amplified by IC1(a). This is wired as an inverting amplifier with the preset VR1 controlling the amount of negative feedback, and therefore the gain. Negative feedback is out of phase with the input and tends to cancel it out, so the higher the value of VR1, the higher the output.

The actual gain of the first stage can be found by dividing VR1 by R1. This circuit gives a maximum voltage gain of 10, which is equal to 20dB. You can use VR1 to set the output level of the circuit so that it matches the unprocessed or bypassed signal from the guitar.

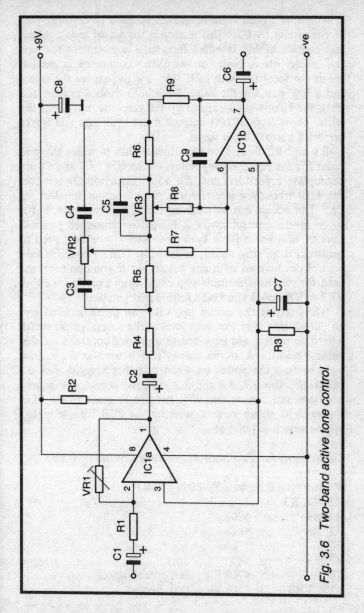

Fig. 3.6 Two-band active tone control

51

Amplifier signals from IC1(a) are coupled to the next part of the circuit by C2. This section is the actual tone control, and consists of the standard Baxandall arrangement for bass and treble. It is basically two filters connected in parallel across the feedback path of IC1(b), a high pass for the treble and a low pass for the bass. With both control pots in mid track the circuit has a reasonably flat response, but needs the initial boost from IC1(a) because it has little gain and works best with a strong input signal.

R3 and R2 form a voltage divider that provides the mid point for the non-inverting inputs of the IC's. C7 and C8 are decoupling capacitors, and the 15pF capacitor C9 removes any high frequency interference. Signal output is taken via C6. The circuit can be built on the PCB shown here, but if space in the control cavity is limited — remember you will have to find room for a battery as well — you may need to construct it on strip board, or a smaller PCB. The active tone control can be used with any guitar, but if you don't feel the need for two tone controls you could swap a preset for either VR2 or VR3 once you find a setting that you like.

When setting the circuit up, VR1 can be adjusted to give an output that is at the same level as the normal guitar signal. Alternatively it could be wired to a pot and control a variable volume boost. A stereo output jack is used in the normal way, to turn the power on when a lead is plugged into the guitar. Figures 3.7, 3.8 and 3.9 show the layout, component positions and connections that need to be made to the PCB. Figure 3.10 shows how to wire up the PCB for use with a bypass switch or pull pot.

Components for Two-band Active Tone Control (Fig.3.6)

Resistors (all 0.25 watt 5% carbon film)
R1, R2, R3   47k
R4, R9   470R
R5, R6   4k7
R7   27k
R8   5k6
VR1   470k log preset potentiometer
VR2, VR3   100k lin potentiometer

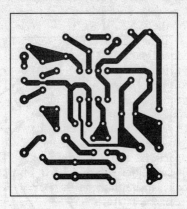

Fig. 3.7   Two-band active tone control PCB layout
(actual size)

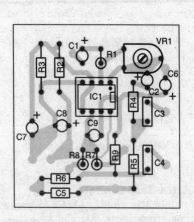

Fig. 3.8   Two-band active tone control components overlay

53

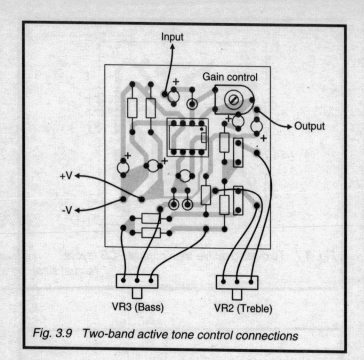

Fig. 3.9 Two-band active tone control connections

Capacitors

C1, C2, C6, C7	1μF 16V electrolytic
C3, C4	3n3 polyester
C5	100nF polyester
C8	100μF 16V electrolytic
C9	15pF ceramic

Semiconductors

TLO72	dual op-amp

Bass Guitar Active Tone Control

Bass guitars with active circuitry are a lot more common than active six string instruments. Bass players seem to have taken to being able to define their sound more accurately. This is probably because a bass is usually played monophonically, i.e.

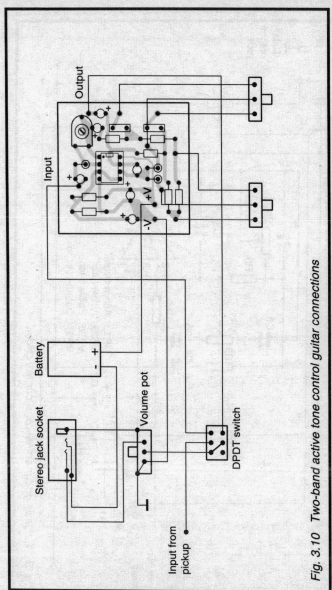

Fig. 3.10 Two-band active tone control guitar connections

Output

Input

Battery

Stereo jack socket

Volume pot

DPDT switch

Input from pickup

+V

-V

55

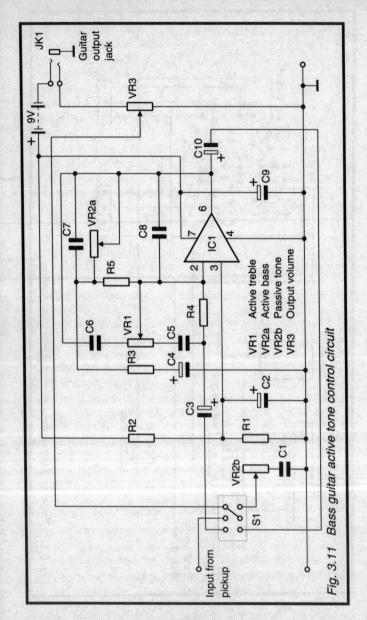

JK1

Guitar output jack

VR3

+ 9V

C10

C9

C7   VR2a   C8   6   7   IC1   4

R5   2   3

VR1   R4   Active treble   VR1
C6   R3   C5   Active bass   VR2a
C4   Passive tone   VR2b
R2   C3   C2   Output volume   VR3
R1

VR2b   C1

S1

Input from pickup

Fig. 3.11 Bass guitar active tone control circuit

56

one note at a time, and the sounds they produce are therefore simpler to modify. Often, particular styles of bass playing need a specific tonal quality to be effective. A jazz player might need a crisp accurate sound, so that each note he plays is clear and defined, while a heavy rock bassist might want a powerful subsonic rumble to counter trebly and overdriven guitars. A lot of bass amps include some sort of parametric or even graphic equaliser to enable the frequency response to be accurately controlled.

The active circuit shown in Figure 3.11 is especially for bass guitar and provides a smooth range of definition over the bass and treble ranges. It can be wired into a guitar with or without a bypass switch, as it produces little gain and only has a small effect on output levels.

The circuit is built around an NE5534 op-amp, wired in inverting mode with the equalising filters connected into the feedback loop in the normal way. If you are not particularly bothered about extremely low noise levels, the 5534 can be replaced by a cheaper TLO71.

The stereo potentiometer VR2 serves as both a passive and active tone control. In the active mode one track is connected, and in passive, the other is used. This means that when the active circuit is bypassed, VR2(b) is connected across the pickup via C1 forming a normal low pass tone control. When the active circuit is switched in, this track is disconnected and the pot VR2a operates as the bass cut/boost control. In passive mode, the active treble control VR1 has no effect.

The volume control is connected across the output of the guitar and operates on both the active and bypassed signals.

If you don't think you are going to need a passive tone control or a bypass switch, the circuit can be simplified and the stereo controls replaced with normal mono logarithmic potentiometers. The input of the active circuit can then be connected to the pickup or pickup selector switch, and the volume control wired to the output in the normal way. If only one active tone control is required, perhaps to utilise a limited number of potentiometer mounting holes, one of the pots can be replaced by a pre-set of the same value, once you decide which control will be least used.

Resistors (all 0.25 watt 5% carbon film)

R1, R2	820k
R3	10k
R4	330k
R5	100k
VR1	1M mono log potentiometer
VR2	100k stereo log potentiometer
VR3	470k mono log potentiometer

Capacitors

C1	47nF polyester
C2, C3, C9	2μ2 16V tantalum bead
C4, C10	10μF 16V tantalum bead
C5	3n3 polyester
C6	560pF polystyrene
C7	68nF polyester
C8	120pF polystyrene

Semiconductors

IC1	NE5534 low noise op-amp

Miscellaneous

JK1	Stereo jack socket
S1	DPDT switch

Seven-band Equaliser

If you want to go over the top with your tone control options, you might consider the seven band EQ circuit shown in Figure 3.12. It would probably be unrealistic to mount all the control pots on the front of a guitar, but it could be built into a small effects type box to sit on top of an amplifier.

It was originally designed with the bass in mind but turned out to be very effective with six string guitars as well. The circuit is essentially passive but has a preamp to make up for the losses that occur as signals pass through it. The preamp is the same as the one described earlier, and has a maximum gain of around 20dB. It feeds seven parallel band pass filters

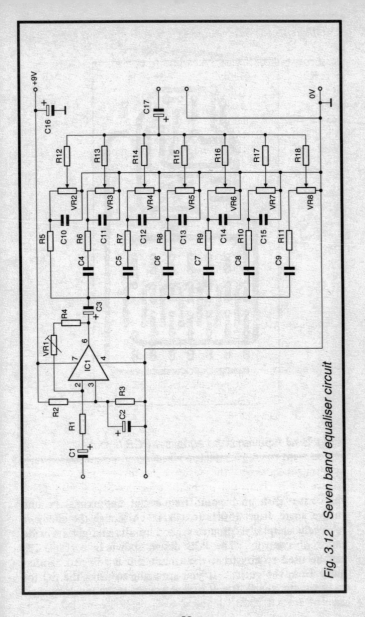

Fig. 3.12 Seven band equaliser circuit

59

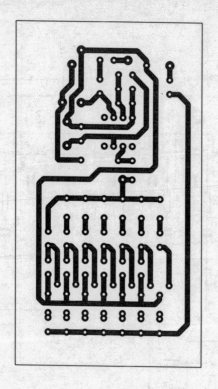

Fig. 3.13   Seven band equaliser PCB layout

that have their mid point frequencies approximately one octave apart, from 150Hz to 10kHz. Although the circuit is relatively simple, it produces good results and gives a wide range of control.   The PCB design shown here (Fig.3.13) can be used to construct the circuit if it is going to be used away from the guitar. If you are going to make the EQ for onboard use the PCB will probably have to be much smaller.

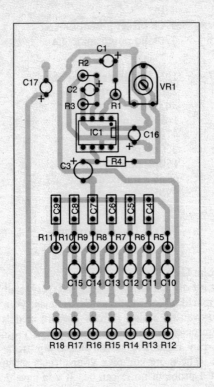

Fig. 3.14 Seven band equaliser component overlay

For an even control action you should use linear potentio-meters. Figure 3.14 shows the components overlay.

Components for Seven-band Equaliser (Fig.3.12)

Resistors (all 0.25 watt 5% carbon film)
R1 – R4   47k
R5, R11   820k

R6 – R10	470k
R12 – R18	470k
VR1	470k preset potentiometer
VR2 – VR8	470k lin potentiometers

Capacitors

C1, C3, C17	1µF 16V tantalum bead
C2, C16	22µF 16V tantalum bead
C10	3n3 polystyrene
C4, C11	1nF ceramic disc
C5, C12	470pF polystyrene
C6, C13	220pF polystyrene
C7, C14	150pF polystyrene
C8, C15	68pF ceramic disc
C9	39pF ceramic disc

Semiconductors

| IC1 | TLO71 low noise op-amp |

Dynamic Noise Gate

If you use a lot of post guitar effects units, especially the older tape echo machines or analogue delay lines, you will know all about unwanted noise. Even modern pedals and rack mounted equipment, though they may be very quiet in their own right, can introduce noise picked up from leads and power lines. The more complex your effects set-up becomes, the more of a problem noise can be. If you have done all you can to make your instrument as silent as possible, by making sure it is screened and earthed correctly, for instance, (see section on noise reduction) it makes sense to try to reduce noise from the next stage in the amplification chain.

There are a number of ways to cut down on background interference introduced before a signal reaches the main amplifier, including EQ filters, low level cut off devices, and even complex microprocessor controlled systems. The dynamic noise gate described here is a cheap and versatile unit that can be used with a guitar and effects chain, as well as other signal sources such as tape recorders. It has the advantage of being relatively easy to build, and requires no setting up. You can use it for recording and on stage, where noise interference from lighting circuits and power cables running close together can be a problem.

The dynamic noise gate shown in Figure 3.15 is designed to be positioned at the end of an effects chain, so that all the unwanted noise signals can be removed before they reach the main amplifier. This positioning is not critical, and you may simply want to use the unit to silence one particularly noisy piece of equipment — an old tape delay for instance — in which case, just connect the unit to the output of whatever you need to gate.

The noise gate works by reducing or expanding the dynamic range of signals passing through it. Noise signals, like background hiss or hum, which are present all the time, can be removed by setting the gate so that they are just below the level at which it starts to open. When wanted signals, which are at a higher level than the background noise, enter the gate, it opens up to allow them to pass with full dynamic range. When the louder signals are present, any background noise is masked. This arrangement is good for musical instruments because it does not simply shut off at a particular level and tends to sound smoother and less noticeable when in use. The lowest level at which the gate starts to open can be set manually.

The circuit for the noise gate is based around an NE571 compander. This IC contains two identical gain control circuits which can be wired as dynamic range expanders or compressors. The NE571 is available with a higher specification as the NE570, but for this kind of application the extra cost of a 570 is not really justified. The main difference between the chips is that the 570 can operate from a higher supply voltage — 24V instead of 18V — and has a slightly better distortion performance.

Signals enter the circuit via C1 and pass through to VR1 which acts as the level control, this can be used to match the input to a variety of sources including instruments, effects pedals and even tape decks if need be. IC1 forms an inverting buffer with its gain set by R1 and R4. The output from the op-amp feeds a 2:1 compression network formed around one half of IC2.

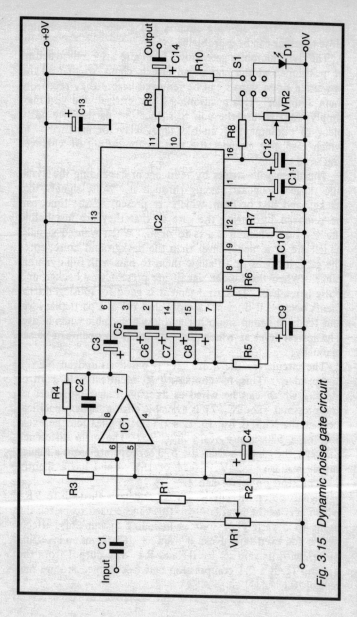

Fig. 3.15 Dynamic noise gate circuit

The capacitors used here are for decoupling the various parts of the circuit, and setting the attack/decay levels in the variable gain section. They need to be of the same value if the two independent sections of the IC are to track each other accurately.

Once compressed, the signal enters the other half of the IC which expands it back to its original level. VR2 is used to set the level of attenuation in the expander's gain control network, creating a cut-off point below which any signal present – noise – has its dynamic range reduced.

The switch S1 is connected to VR2 and can disconnect the control if the noise gate needs to be bypassed. With VR2 out of the circuit, all signals are passed with full dynamic range at the level set by the input attenuator. This allows the unit to be switched in and out without introducing more noise into the system in the form of clicks and thumps. R8 is as an endstop for the effect control.

With the gate turned off, the unit acts as a low noise pre-amp. D1 is connected to one half of the DPDT bypass switch to indicate when the gate is turned on, and has R10 as a current limiting resistor.

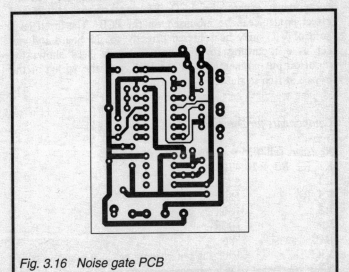

Fig. 3.16   Noise gate PCB

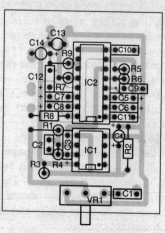

Fig. 3.17 Noise gate component overlay

Figures 3.16 and 3.17 show a PCB design and component overlay that can be used to build the noise gate. All the components except the LED, limiting resistor, switch and effect control can be mounted on the PCB. The input level control VR1 may be soldered directly to the board and can act as a mounting for the unit. Figure 3.18 shows the input/output connections to the PCB, and the wiring of the bypass switch to the effects control.

Components for Dynamic Noise Gate (Fig.3.15)

Resistors (all 0.25 watt 5% carbon film)
R1, R2, R3, R7	47k
R4	820k
R5, R6	15k
R8	100k
R9	100R
R10	5k6
VR1	100k log potentiometer
VR2	1M log potentiometer

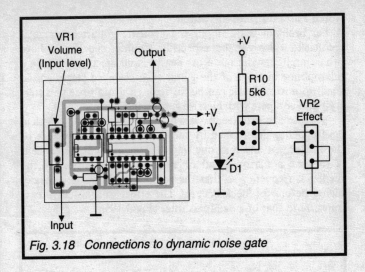

Fig. 3.18   Connections to dynamic noise gate

Capacitors

C1	100nF polyester
C2	68pF ceramic
C3, C5, C6, C7, C8, C9, C11, C12	$1\mu F$ 16V tantalum bead
C4	$10\mu F$ 16V electrolytic
C10	47nF polyester
C13	$100\mu F$ 16V electrolytic
C14	$2\mu2$ 16V electrolytic

Semiconductors

IC1	TLO72
IC2	NE570 or NE571
D1	LED

Miscellaneous

S1	DPDT mini toggle switch
	16 and 8 pin IC sockets

Notch Filter for Acoustic Guitar

A big problem with amplifying acoustic guitars on stage is feedback. This can be especially troublesome if you have other amplifiers and monitors nearby, and are trying to use a microphone in front of the guitar. On cramped stages and in small rooms feedback can be difficult to avoid once you start trying to compete with electric guitars and drums.

Because acoustic feedback will begin to occur at a particular frequency determined by factors such as the resonance of the instrument and mic, one way you can attempt to reduce it is to have a narrow band or 'notch' filter to attenuate the feedback frequency so that the volume level can be generally higher before feedback occurs. The effect of a notch filter is opposite to that of a bandpass filter (Fig.3.19).

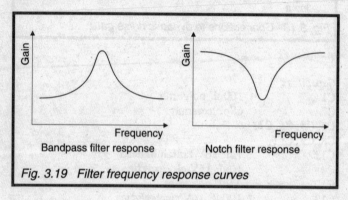

Fig. 3.19   Filter frequency response curves

The circuit shown in Figure 3.20 is an active notch that can be used in some situations to cut down on, or get rid of acoustic feedback. Because the frequency at which feedback occurs will tend to change depending on how the guitar is positioned, surroundings, etc., the location of the rejection band, or notch, can be varied.

Signals are fed into the filter from a mic or acoustic pickup via the input jack JK1, they are then amplified by IC1 which is connected in the conventional way, as an inverting amplifier. R2 and R4 provide the mid rail voltage for the non-inverting pin of the IC. As the gain of the unit will need regular adjustment for different instruments or mics, its probably a good

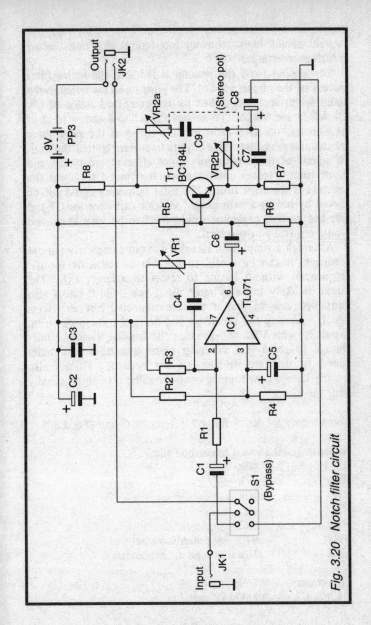

Fig. 3.20 Notch filter circuit

69

idea to use a potentiometer rather than a preset for VR1. C4 gets rid of any high frequency interference that might occur at high gain settings.

The output from the preamp is fed into the active filter section of the circuit via C6. The position of the notch in the audio spectrum is controlled by the combined action of C7, C9, VR2a and VR2b. To keep the notch to a narrow band of frequencies, the two resistors have to be of the same value relative to each other. This is quite important so that the overall sound of the instrument is not affected too much, and means that a stereo potentiometer is required to adjust the resistors at the same time. The filter frequency could also be moved by having a twin ganged variable capacitor for C7 and C9, but such a capacitor would need to be very large, and would not really be practical.

Although a simple unit like this will not completely remove feedback, it can be useful to be able to attenuate specific frequencies without having to resort to a larger EQ. The circuit is likely to be of most use if you build it into a self-contained case so that it can be connected like an effects pedal. Moving the notch up and down the audio spectrum manually with VR2 will produce the familiar 'phaser' effect, though to get a rich sweeping sound a number of notches tuned to different frequencies are needed. Phasers also usually have a slow running control oscillator to automatically shift the filters.

Components for Notch Filter for Acoustic Guitar (Fig.3.20)

Resistors (all 0.25 watt 5% carbon film)

R1, R2, R3, R4	47k
R5	27k
R6	10k
R7	1k
R8	2k2
VR1	470k log potentiometer
VR2	10k stereo lin potentiometer

Capacitors

C1, C6, C8	1μF 16V tantalum

C2	100μF 16V electrolytic
C3, C7, C9	100nF polyester
C4	64pF ceramic
C5	10μF 16V electrolytic

Semiconductors

| IC1 | TLO71 op-amp |
| Tr1 | BC184L low noise NPN |

Miscellaneous

JK1	mono jack socket
JK2	stereo jack socket
S1	DPDT switch

Active Equaliser for Acoustic Guitar

The seven band EQ described earlier can be very effective, but is still of passive design, which means it can only be used to attenuate frequencies, not boost them.

Figure 3.21 is a four band EQ that offers a wider degree of signal control through the use of an independent active filter for each frequency band. In this example the bands are centred on 64Hz (VR2), 500Hz (VR3), 4kHz (VR4) and 16kHz (VR5), which gives a fairly even selection of bass, mid and treble frequencies. By changing the capacitor values in the filter circuits, different centre frequencies can be obtained (Figs 3.22 and 3.23). You will notice from the table that the value of Cap A is always ten times that of Cap B. The circuit was intended for possible mounting inside an acoustic guitar but could quite easily be used as an external unit. If required, extra filters can be added in parallel to the existing ones, to increase the number of bands.

The action of the EQ is fairly straightforward. Signals enter a variable gain preamp formed around IC1 via JK1 and C1. VR1 controls the gain of this section with R4 acting as an endstop for the control. The high value of VR1 means that the preamp section can have a lot of gain. This allows for low output piezoelectric contact pickups to be connected directly to the circuit.

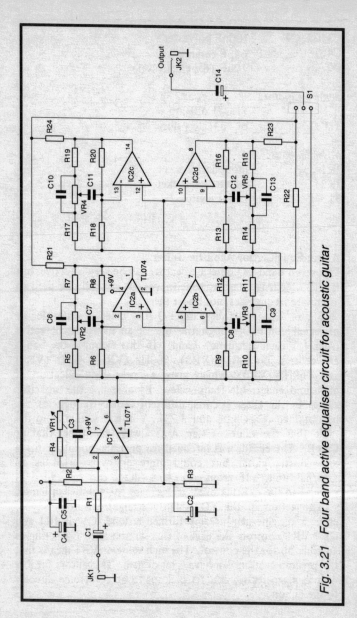

Fig. 3.21 Four band active equaliser circuit for acoustic guitar

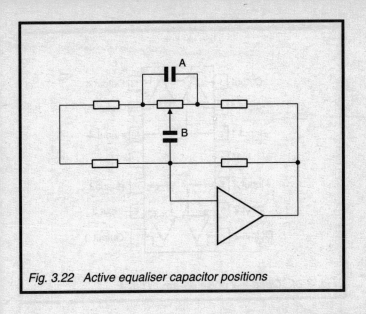

Fig. 3.22 Active equaliser capacitor positions

Cap A	Cap B	Centre frequency
330nF	33nF	16Hz
180nF	18nF	32Hz
100nF	10nF	64Hz
47nF	4n7	125Hz
22nF	2n2	250Hz
15nF	1n5	500Hz
5n6	560pF	1kHz
2n7	270pF	2kHz
1n5	150pF	4kHz
680pF	68pF	8kHz
220pF	22pF	16kHz
100pF	10pF	32kHz

Fig. 3.23 Table of capacitor values for active equaliser

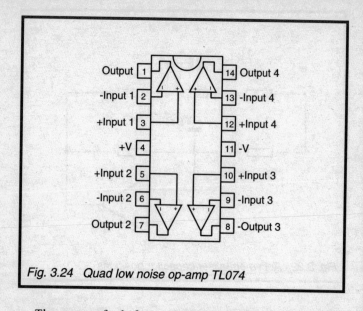

Fig. 3.24   Quad low noise op-amp TL074

The preamp feeds four active band pass filters connected in parallel. In this case based around a TLO74 quad low noise op-amp (Fig.3.24). This IC is simply four TLO71s in one 14 pin package. The filters will work with most general purpose op-amps, though low noise ICs should be used if possible. It is worthwhile having double or quad components if you need more than four filters, as it saves on PCB space.

The output from each filter is fed to the switch S1 through resistors R21 — R24. The switch selects either the equalised output from the filters, or the output from the preamp. This allows comparisons to be made between the flat and equalised signals. C14 couples the switch to the output jack JK2.

Components for Active Equaliser for Acoustic Guitar (Fig.3.21)

Resistors (all 0.25 watt 5% carbon film)
R1, R2, R3, R4   47k
R5, R7, R9   10k

R12, R13, R16, R17, R19	10k
R6, R8, R10, R11, R14, R15, R18, R20	820k
R21, R22, R23, R24	56k
VR1	2M2 log potentiometer
VR2 – VR5	100k lin potentiometers

Capacitors

C1, C14	1μF 16V electrolytic
C2	10μF 16V electrolytic
C3	15pF ceramic
C4	100μF 16V electrolytic
C5, C6	100nF polyester
C7	10nF polyester
C8	1n5 polyester
C9	15nF polyester
C10	1n5 polyester
C11	150pF polystyrene
C12	22pF polystyrene
C13	220pF polystyrene

Semiconductors

| IC1 | TLO71 op-amp |
| IC2 | TLO74 quad op-amp |

Power Indicators

If a guitar has active circuitry built in, it is useful to know when the circuit is operational, or when the power is connected. As most active guitars utilise the jack socket as a switch for the overall power on/off it is easy to forget to remove the lead when you finish playing, and drain the battery. The simple LED indicator shown in Figure 3.25 can be used to show when power is connected to the active circuit. It is best to use low power LEDs so they don't drain the battery. The current limiting resistor R1 can be chosen depending on the supply voltage being used. The table overleaf gives some

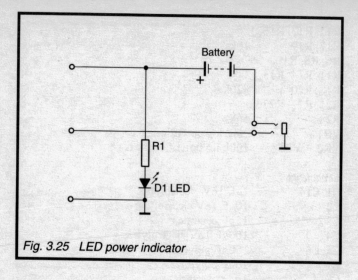

Fig. 3.25 LED power indicator

Supply Voltage	R1 Value
3	220
6	820
9	1k5
18	3k3

voltages and values for R1. If you do not want to have a power indicator that stays on all the time, but simply need to know when the active circuit is in operation, you can connect a LED to the bypass switch. Figure 3.26 shows a simple way of doing this, using the normal DPDT bypass switch. One disadvantage of this method is that only the output of the active circuit is disconnected when the switch is operated, which can sometimes create more noise than having both the input and output switched. If this is a real problem it may be helpful to reduce the value of the active circuit input and output capacitors to around 0.1μF. A better method is shown in Figure 3.27. This circuit uses a three pole change-over switch to completely disconnect the

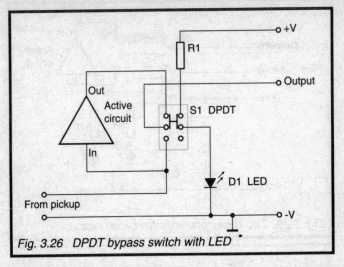

Fig. 3.26 DPDT bypass switch with LED

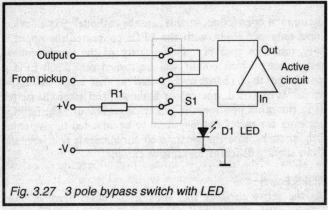

Fig. 3.27 3 pole bypass switch with LED

active circuit, as well as operating the indicator LED. Three and four pole switches are available in both rotary and mini toggle styles.

Figure 3.28 is combined power on, and active circuit indicator. It uses a bi-coloured LED, which will emit two different colours – red and green for instance – depending on which element is connected. Both elements usually share

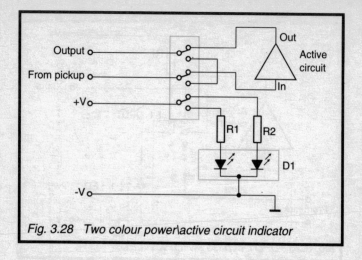

Fig. 3.28 Two colour power\active circuit indicator

a common connection, in this case the cathode. Some devices have only two leads, with the LEDs connected the opposite way round in parallel. The polarity of the supply voltage determining which colour will be turned on. Each LED is connected to a change-over switch so that when the active circuit is bypassed, one colour is shown, and when the switch is in the other position, the LED changes colour. The limiting resistors for each LED may have to be adjusted to give equal brightness because the separate colour elements will generally draw slightly different amounts of current.

Mains Power
As the active circuitry that ends up in guitars becomes more complicated, so the power consumption tends to rise, and the use of batteries becomes more expensive. If you have a mains adaptor to run effects pedals, it is easy to use it for the active circuitry in the guitar as well. Power supplies are so cheap that it is hardly worth building one from scratch.

The layout in Figure 3.29 shows how to connect an effects power supply to run an active guitar as well as a couple of effects pedals, using a simple junction box.

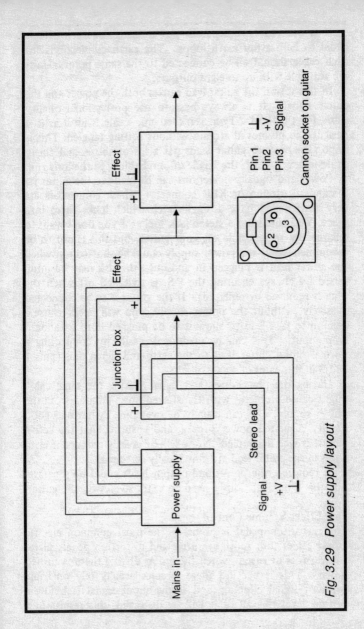

Fig. 3.29 Power supply layout

Power supply

Mains in

Junction box

Effect

Effect

Stereo lead

Signal
+V
⊥

⊥ +V Signal

Pin 1
Pin 2
Pin 3

Cannon socket on guitar

It is best to have separate power leads for each effects pedal to help avoid earth loops. The earth connections for each cable should all be connected to the same point. Units are available with up to eight outputs.

In this set-up the guitar lead carries both the power and the guitar signal. It is always best to use professional quality cable for this lead. Twin screened mic cable is ideal as it is designed to be moved around without getting tangled. This is important because guitar leads get a lot of abuse, and cheap cable is never worth the hassle of unreliability in the long run.

Power and signal connections can be made to the guitar via a standard cannon or XLR connector. These connectors are very rugged and have a small catch which locks them into place. You could use a stereo jack socket if you don't want to enlarge the socket hole on your guitar, but this is not to be recommended as the power supply could be shorted out when the guitar lead is plugged in and out, (the risk may be minimised by always ensuring the P.S. is switched off when the plug is removed or replaced). If the guitar is to be connected passively, without the power supply, you will need to use a cannon to jack lead to allow it to be plugged in to a standard amp input. This can be made very easily by connecting a normal mono guitar lead to the earth and signal pins (pins 1 and 3 in this case) of a cannon plug.

Having the power lines and signal sharing the same cable might cause problems with transferred noise coming from the power supply. This can usually be overcome by having a good quality regulated power supply, and ensuring that the active circuit is well decoupled. Noise will be greatly reduced if both wires in the guitar lead are individually screened.

If required, the power and output leads could be separate, but this would obviously need an extra socket on the guitar.

Post Effect Volume Control
The distortion pedal is probably the most common electric guitar effect, but most overdrive and distortion pedals suffer from a loss of sustain when the guitar driving them is turned down. This is because these circuits usually rely on some form of signal clipping, and if the input signal is below a certain level not all of it will be distorted, this results in a

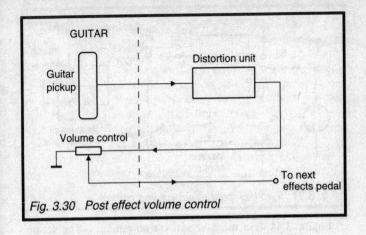

GUITAR

Guitar
pickup

Distortion unit

Volume control

To next
effects pedal

Fig. 3.30   Post effect volume control

weak effect. Some circuits get round the problem by using an automatic gain control to keep the signal levels constant, but many simple units don't have this.

To get the maximum effect from a distortion or overdrive the input should be as high as possible, which means that if you want the same quality of effect over the whole volume range, you need to have a volume control that operates on the output of the effect, rather than the output of the guitar (Fig.3.30). One way of achieving this is to have a volume pedal at the end of the effects chain. If you still want volume adjustments to be made on the guitar — pedals can be awkward to adjust on stage and tie you to one place — you can rewire your guitar with a post-effects volume control.

There are a couple of ways you can do this. One is to replace the volume pot in the guitar with the output level pot from the distortion pedal.

Signals from the pickup go straight to the pedal without being attenuated, then come back to the guitar and pass through the output level control before going back out and on to the next effect. This set-up can be really effective, giving a constant level of distortion at any volume setting, but limits the types of sounds the guitar can produce. It is probably best done only if your playing style requires constant distortion.

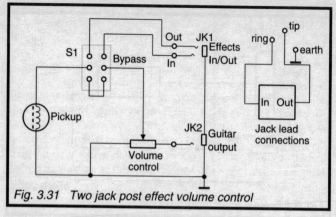

Fig. 3.31   Two jack post effect volume control

Figure 3.31 is a more versatile arrangement. The set-up has two output jacks on the guitar, one stereo, for the input/output signals to the effects pedal, and a normal mono socket for the guitar output. This set-up allows the guitar to be used in the normal way, as well as to control an effects pedal. The DPDT switch S1 channels signals from the pickup via the effects loop, or straight through the volume control to the output. This allows S1 to act as a bypass when the effects lead is plugged in. With no effect connected to the guitar, S1 will simply turn the output on and off.

Chapter 4

MISCELLANEOUS

Noise Reduction

The term 'noise' refers to any part of a signal that is not supposed to be there, i.e. supply line ripple or radio interference.

As far as electric guitars are concerned, the most common and annoying form of noise interference is likely to be mains hum picked up by badly shielded circuitry on an instrument, or by faulty leads and connectors.

Leads and Connectors

To reduce noise introduced on the guitar lead, or shorter effects pedal connectors, you should always use the highest quality cables you can afford. Having cheap cables is a false economy, especially if you do a lot of gigging, because they will not last as long as their professional equivalents, and often do not work as well to start off with.

Any cable that gets connected to an amplifier input must be screened. This includes all connections between effects pedals and all mic leads. The only cables that do not normally need to be screened are ones carrying high level signals such as the ones between amps and speakers. This may seem obvious, but I have come across people using three core mains cable, and even bell wire as guitar leads.

Along with the cables, the jack plugs are important, because unless they are in good condition, connections to and from the instrument may not be made properly and this could result in poor signal quality as well as increased noise. Jack plugs should, if possible, be made of metal. Soft plastic moulded plugs are sometimes fitted to manufactured guitar leads, and these seem to be quite effective, though they can be troublesome if the plastic is moulded inaccurately or has burrs on the face that makes contact with the socket. If you make up your own leads, avoid using the hard plastic cased jack plugs, as they can be brittle and will easily break if stood on or pulled too hard. This type of plug is only really suitable for home use, and should never be trusted on stage.

A good connector to fit to a guitar lead is a jack with a built in switch. When this type of jack is unplugged from the instrument, the signal wire is connected to earth, avoiding loud clicks and thumps which might damage speakers. A switched jack is useful on stage if a lead needs to be swapped from one instrument or effect to another while it is still 'live'.

When soldering jack plugs to cables, try not to use too much heat as the insulation may melt, causing a possible short circuit between the conductors, or weaknesses in the plastic that may fail later. It is usually best to strip the screen and central conductor to the right lengths, and tin the wire ends. The connectors in the jack plug can also be tinned so that only a small amount of heat is needed to melt the joints together. Remember to slide the outer case of the plug onto the cable before you connect up the lead.

The cable retaining clip at the end of the earth connector should be squeezed round the outer layer of the cable, not just the screen, as this may cause unnecessary wear. Take care not to over-tighten the retainer, as it may cut through and damage the insulation.

Screening the Guitar

One of the best ways to eliminate induced noise from a guitar is to screen all the control and pickup cavities with metal foil. This can be really effective, even on guitars with humbucking pickups.

To screen the cavities you will need to strip the guitar completely so that every internal surface is exposed. It is then just a case of sticking metal foil onto the wood to create a completely screened compartment for the electronics. Screening foil is available on reels with one side coated in adhesive. This is very easy to use and makes for a neat job. It is possible to do the job with ordinary tin foil and glue, but this can be messy. With the cavities screened, you should screw in a small lug or terminal to act as an earth connection for the foil. The lug should be connected to the earth terminal on the jack socket, or the top of an earthed control pot. Without a good earth connection, the screening will be useless and may even increase noise levels.

The underside of the control cavity lid should also be coated with foil, and, if possible, a wire taken from it to an earth connection. If you can not make a direct connection to the lid, make sure its foil comes into contact with the foil in the control cavity when it is screwed down. If the lid is not earthed the compartment will not be fully screened.

The pickup routs and scratch plate can be screened in the same way as the control cavities, with separate connections being made to a common earth point.

If required, the pickups themselves can be screened by putting a layer of foil round the coil windings, and connecting it to earth. This will probably not be necessary if the pickup already has a metal case.

When rewiring a stripped down guitar, remember to replace the bridge earth connection, as it is important in reducing noise that may be picked up on the strings. Having the strings earthed is also a good safety point, especially if you use a valve amp. The bridge earth connection is usually just a piece of wire held in place under the bridge and attached to the common earth point.

Setting Up A Guitar

If you have attempted to build active circuitry into a guitar, or altered the pickups and wiring, you will probably have disturbed the action and intonation settings, and may need to do a set-up to get the guitar playing correctly. This will be most useful if you have moved the bridge or neck. There are a number of things that can be done to a guitar for a full set-up, including levelling the frets and setting the string heights at the nut, but these are beyond the scope of this book. The set-up described here is quite basic, and assumes that the instrument does not need serious attention.

Although doing a set-up may appear a little daunting if you have never done one before, it is really quite straight-forward if you use an electronic tuner. It is possible to do a rought set-up without a tuner, but unless you possess a very good sense of pitch it may be difficult to match the fretted notes and harmonics when adjusting the string lengths.

A set-up should be done using new strings, in the following order:

1. **Truss rod** — to get the neck straight.
2. **Action** — to adjust the distance between the strings and the finger board.
3. **Intonation** — to make the strings the right length so that notes are fretted in tune along the whole of the neck.
4. **Pickups** — to set the pickups at the right height, and adjust the poles correctly for the string gauge being used.

The first step in a set-up is to get the neck straight so that the strings lie almost parallel to it along the whole of its length. To do this you have to tighten up or lossen the truss rod adjuster (Fig.4.1) which will be at either the head stock or neck rout end of the neck.

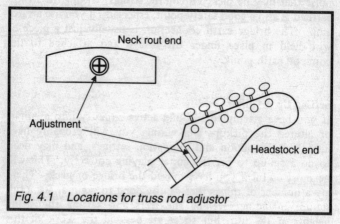

Fig. 4.1   *Locations for truss rod adjustor*

Virtually all electric guitars and most steel string acoustics will have a truss rod. Classical guitars do not need them because they have low tension nylon or gut strings. You should never put steel strings onto a classical guitar unless you want to snap the neck.

The function of the truss rod is simply to strengthen the neck so that the strings do not pull it out of shape. This allows electric guitar necks to be relatively thin. The rod itself is usually made of steel and about 4 or 5mm in diameter. It lies in a slot under the finger board, anchored at one end. An adjuster at the other end allows the effect it has to be varied to take into account factors such as the gauge of the strings and any warping that might occur. The truss rod adjuster will probably have either a large cross headed screw arrangement, or a slug to fit an Allen key into. Do not try to adjust the truss rod without the right tool because you may damage the adjuster. On some guitars the adjuster is positioned quite low in the neck and gets hidden by the neck rout which means taking the neck off to adjust it. This can be a bit more time-consuming and fiddly because you will not be able to tell if the neck is correctly set until you put the strings back on and have the instrument at concert pitch.

You can adjust the neck with the strings on the guitar if you wish but it is usually easier with them hanging loose or removed. It helps if you have some sort of straight edge to hand, like a long steel ruler. This should be placed edgeways along the length of the neck so that it touches the tops of the frets.

By holding the neck up to the light you will be able to see if it is straight by the amount of light showing under the ruler. If there is a relatively large gap towards the middle of the neck you should tighten up the adjuster (clockwise) until the gap is reduced. If the neck tends to bow back you should adjust it the other way.

When the neck is adjusted without the strings in place you should try and put a slight back bow into it so that the tension of the strings at concert pitch will pull it straight. You may have to make a few attempts at this if you have never done it before.

With the strings on the guitar, a good way to tell if the neck is straight is to hold down the first and last fret of the bottom E at the same time. If everything is straight, the distance between the string and the 12th fret should be just under 1mm.

When you make truss rod adjustments, the most important thing to remember is not over-tighten the adjuster or you may strip the thread. This could be expensive to fix as it might involve removing the finger board.

When you have the neck straight you can move on to set the action. The action is the distance between the strings and the tops of the frets. People usually try to reduce this to the absolute minimum so that the guitar is faster and easier to play, but how high you set the action is up to you. An average distance is likely to be around 2mm at the 12th fret, if you play a lot of slide guitar you will probably want it higher.

The action can be set by raising or lowering the adjusters on the bridge saddles (Fig.4.2). Some types of guitar do not have adjustment for individual strings, and rely on simply

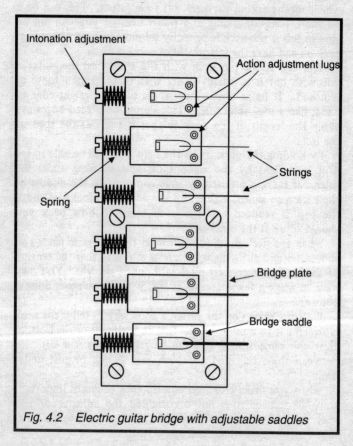

Intonation adjustment

Action adjustment lugs

Strings

Spring

Bridge plate

Bridge saddle

Fig. 4.2   Electric guitar bridge with adjustable saddles

raising and lowering the mountings at the ends of the bridge. If you have an instrument with a floating trem it is probably better not to fiddle with it unless you know what you are doing as they are notoriously difficult to set up. When you come to alter the action you might find it easier if the strings are quite loose, as the adjustment lugs are often very small and awkward to move with the full string tension pressing down on them. When setting the relative heights of the strings, you should aim to follow the camber of the finger board so that all the strings are the same distance from the frets (Fig.4.3).

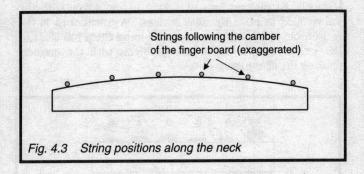

Fig. 4.3   String positions along the neck

The next part of the set-up is the intonation. This adjustment is much easier to do accurately with a guitar tuner. A stroboscopic tuner is best, if you have access to one, but as they are very expensive, most people have to make do with a normal electronic tuner. The purpose of setting the intonation is to adjust the overall lengths of the strings so that the mid point harmonic and the middle of the neck (12th fret) fall in the same place. If the intonation is not accurately set, the guitar will not play in tune. A chord that sounds OK played at the first fret will be out of tune played an octave higher, at the twelfth fret.

To set the intonation, start with the top E, and using the tuner, bring it up to concert pitch. When the string has settled — it helps to stretch new strings as you fit them — play a harmonic at the twelfth fret.

As the twelfth fret is positioned right in the middle of the string, the note played here should be the same as the harmonic, and an octave higher than the open string. If the tuner shows that the fretted note is flat in relation to the harmonic it indicates that the string is too long, and the bridge saddle should be moved forward to shorten it until the harmonic and the fretted note are in tune. If the fretted note is sharp in relation to the harmonic, the bridge saddle can be moved back to lengthen the string. All the other strings should be done in the same way.

To adjust the height of the pickups in relation to the strings simply use the mounting screws at either side of the case. Virtually all pickups have this kind of mounting, with the screws held in place by small springs. As mentioned in the section on pickups, it is best not to move them too close to the strings or you might have problems with the magnets choking the lighter gauges.

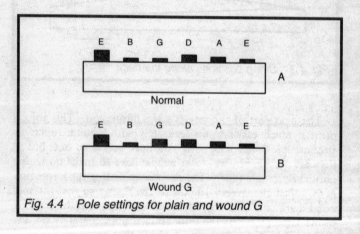

Fig. 4.4   Pole settings for plain and wound G

If you have pickups with adjustable poles, they can be set up to give fine adjustment of the relative string volumes. Figure 4.4 shows two basic settings for the pole pieces. 'A' is for strings with a plain G, and 'B' is for a set with a wound G. A plain G string is louder than a wound one, so the pole piece needs to be raised or lowered to compensate for this.

Semiconductor Pinouts

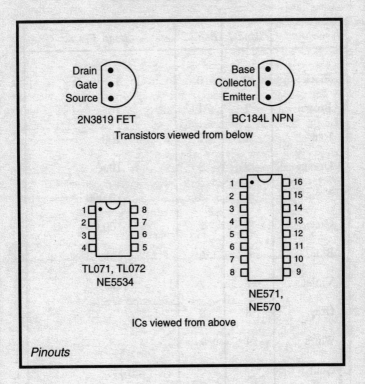

Drain
Gate
Source

2N3819 FET

Base
Collector
Emitter

BC184L NPN

Transistors viewed from below

1 8
2 7
3 6
4 5

TL071, TL072
NE5534

1 16
2 15
3 14
4 13
5 12
6 11
7 10
8 9

NE571,
NE570

ICs viewed from above

Pinouts

Resistor Colour Code

Colour	Band 1	Band 2	Band 3 (×)
Black	0	0	1
Brown	1	1	10
Red	2	2	100
Orange	3	3	1000
Yellow	4	4	10,000
Green	5	5	100,000
Blue	6	6	1M
Violet	7	7	10M
Grey	8	8	
White	9	9	
Gold			0.1
Silver			0.01